DRIVING STANDARDS AGENCY
SAFE DRIVING FOR LIFE

the official DSA
THEORY
TEST REVISION PAPERS
for Car Drivers

London: TSO

Written and compiled by the Publications Unit of the Driving Standards Agency (DSA).

Questions and answers are compiled by the Question Development Team of the DSA.

Published with the permission of the Driving Standards Agency on behalf of the Controller of Her Majesty's Stationery Office.

© Crown Copyright 2006

First published 2004
Third edition 2006

ISBN-13 978 011 552775 3
ISBN-10 011 552775 3

A CIP catalogue record for this book is available from the British Library.

Other titles in the Driving Skills series

The Official DSA Theory Test for Car Drivers
The Official DSA Guide to Learning to Drive
Helping Learners to Practise - the official DSA guide
The Official DSA Guide to Driving - the essential skills
The Official DSA Guide to Learning to Ride
The Official DSA Guide to Riding - the essential skills
The Official DSA Theory Test for Drivers of Large Vehicles
The Official DSA Guide to Driving Buses and Coaches
The Official DSA Guide to Driving Goods Vehicles
The Official DSA Guide to Tractor and Specialist Vehicle Driving Tests
The Official DSA Theory Test for Car Drivers (CD-Rom)
The Official DSA Theory Test for Motorcyclists (CD-Rom)
The Official DSA Theory Test for Drivers of Large Vehicles (CD-Rom)
The Official DSA Guide to Hazard Perception (DVD) (also available on VHS)
Prepare for your Practical Driving Test (DVD)

Every effort has been made to ensure that the information contained in this publication is accurate at the time of going to press. The Stationery Office cannot be held responsible for any inaccuracies. Information in this book is for guidance only.

All metric and imperial conversions in this book are approximate.

Directgov

Directgov is the place to find all government motoring information and services. From logbooks to licensing, from driving tests to road tax, go to:

www.direct.gov.uk/motoring

Theory and practical tests
(Bookings and enquiries)

Online **www.dsa.gov.uk**
DSA **0870 0101 372**
Fax **0870 0104 372**
Minicom **0870 0106 372**
Welsh speakers **0870 0100 372**

DVTA (Northern Ireland)
Theory test **0845 600 6700**
Practical test **0870 247 2471**

Driving Standards Agency
(Headquarters)

www.dsa.gov.uk

Stanley House, 56 Talbot Street, Nottingham NG1 5GU

Tel **0115 901 2500**
Fax **0115 901 2510**

Driver & Vehicle Testing Agency
(Headquarters)

www.dvtani.gov.uk

Balmoral Road, Belfast BT12 6QL

Tel **02890 681 831**
Fax **02890 665 520**

Driver & Vehicle Licensing Agency
(GB licence enquiries)

www.dvla.gov.uk

Longview Road, Swansea SA6 7JL

Tel **0870 240 0009**
Fax **01792 783 071**
Minicom **01792 782 787**

Driver & Vehicle Licensing in Northern Ireland

www.dvlni.gov.uk

County Hall, Castlerock Road, Coleraine BT51 3TB

Tel **02870 341 469**
24 hour tel **0345 111 222**
Minicom **02870 341 380**

The theory test

Test overview

The theory test is a computer-based test and has a multiple choice part followed by a hazard perception part. You need to pass both parts of the theory test at the same sitting to get your theory test pass certificate.

For the multiple choice part, you choose your answers to 35 questions by simply touching the screen. The touch-screen system has been carefully designed to make it easy to use. You can practise for up to 15 minutes before the test starts, staff at the test centre will be on hand to help you if you have any difficulties. Only one question appears on the screen at a time and you select the answer by simply touching the screen. You can move backwards and forwards through the questions and go back to questions that you want to look at again.

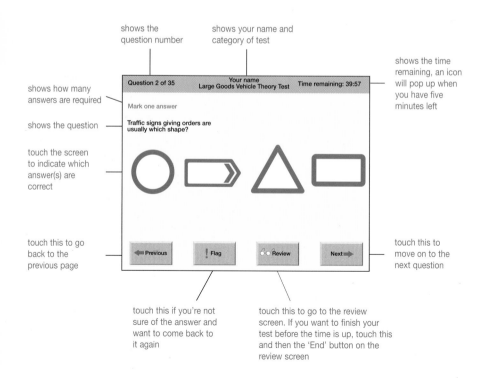

shows the question number

shows your name and category of test

shows the time remaining, an icon will pop up when you have five minutes left

shows how many answers are required

shows the question

touch the screen to indicate which answer(s) are correct

touch this to go back to the previous page

Question 2 of 35 — Your name — Large Goods Vehicle Theory Test — Time remaining: 39:57

Mark one answer

Traffic signs giving orders are usually which shape?

Previous | Flag | Review | Next

touch this to move on to the next question

touch this if you're not sure of the answer and want to come back to it again

touch this to go to the review screen. If you want to finish your test before the time is up, touch this and then the 'End' button on the review screen

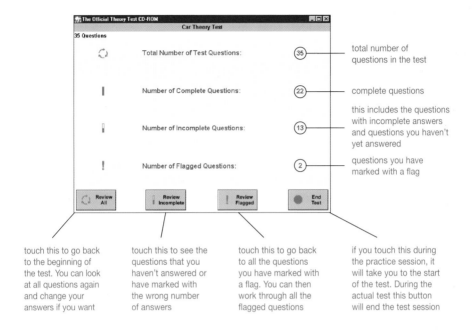

The Official Theory Test CD-ROM

Car Theory Test

35 Questions

Total Number of Test Questions: (35) — total number of questions in the test

Number of Complete Questions: (22) — complete questions

(13) — this includes the questions with incomplete answers and questions you haven't yet answered

Number of Incomplete Questions:

Number of Flagged Questions: (2) — questions you have marked with a flag

Review All | Review Incomplete | Review Flagged | End Test

touch this to go back to the beginning of the test. You can look at all questions again and change your answers if you want

touch this to see the questions that you haven't answered or have marked with the wrong number of answers

touch this to go back to all the questions you have marked with a flag. You can then work through all the flagged questions

if you touch this during the practice session, it will take you to the start of the test. During the actual test this button will end the test session

It's easy to change your answer - the system will alert you if you have not completely answered a question.

You will have 40 minutes to complete the multiple-choice part of the test and you must answer at least 30 questions correctly to pass.

Preparing for your test

All the questions you could be asked in the multiple choice part of the theory test are detailed in *The Official DSA Theory Test for Car Drivers* book. It also includes an explanation of why each answer is correct.

The Official DSA Theory Test for Car Drivers (CD-Rom) contains all this and also allows you to sit realistic mock exams and to create customised tests tailored to target your weaker areas.

The Official DSA Guide to Hazard Perception (DVD) is the ideal way to prepare for the hazard perception part of the theory test. The fully interactive DVD contains clear guidance on how to recognise and respond to hazards on the road. It's packed with useful tips, quizzes, expert advice and includes official DSA hazard perception video clips with feedback on your performance.

Booking your theory test

Theory test centres

There are over 150 theory test centres throughout England, Scotland and Wales, and six in Northern Ireland. Most people have a test centre within 20 miles of their home, but this will vary depending on the density of population in your area.

Test centres are usually open on weekdays, some evenings and some Saturdays.

If you require a theory test in a language other than English or provision for special needs you must state your needs when you book your test.

The easiest ways to book your test are online or by phone, but you can also book by post.

Booking online or by telephone

By using these methods you'll be given the date and time of your test immediately. You can book online at www.direct.gov.uk/motoring (for Northern Ireland use www.dvtani.gov.uk)

To book by telephone, call 0870 0101 372 (0845 600 6700 for Northern Ireland).

If you're deaf and use a minicom machine, call 0870 0106 372 and if you are a Welsh speaker, call 0870 0100 372.

When booking your test you will need your

- DVLA or DVLNI driving licence number
- credit or debit card details (the card holder must book the test). We accept Mastercard, Visa, Delta, Switch/Maestro, Visa Electron and Solo.

You'll be given a booking number and sent an appointment letter that you should receive within eight days.

Booking by post

If you prefer to book by post, you'll need to fill in an application form. These are available from theory test centres, driving test centres, or your instructor may have one.

You should normally receive an appointment letter within ten days of posting your application form.

Using the revision test papers

The revision papers in this book give you an opportunity to test yourself on paper before you take your test. The questions are graded just as they are in the real test, each paper includes a proportionate number taken from each section of the total bank of theory test questions.

You should study *The Official DSA Theory Test for Car Drivers* before taking the sample tests on the following pages.

Instructions

For each question you must find the right answer (or answers) and circle the bullet (or bullets). The answers to the questions are given on p50-54.

To pass each test you must get 30 or more answers correct.

Don't forget that the real test has a time limit of 40 minutes for the multiple choice part.

The two samples below show how the questions should be completed. The number of answers that should be marked is shown on the right hand side of the bar at the top of each question:

3.37   *Mark two answers*

As a driver you can cause more damage to the environment by

⊙ choosing a fuel-efficient vehicle
◎ making a lot of short journeys
⊙ driving in as high a gear as possible
◎ accelerating as quickly as possible
⊙ having your vehicle regularly serviced

11.60   *Mark one answer*

What does this sign mean?

⊙ Cyclists must dismount
⊙ Cycles are not allowed
◎ Cycle route ahead
⊙ Cycle in single file

Revision paper one

You take some cough medicine given to you by a friend. What should you do before driving?

- ⊙ Ask your friend if taking the medicine affected their driving
- ⊙ Drink some strong coffee one hour before driving
- ⊙ Check the label to see if the medicine will affect your driving
- ⊙ Drive a short distance to see if the medicine is affecting your driving

You are coming up to a roundabout. A cyclist is signalling to turn right. What should you do?

- ⊙ Overtake on the right
- ⊙ Give a horn warning
- ⊙ Signal the cyclist to move across
- ⊙ Give the cyclist plenty of room

It is a very windy day and you are about to overtake a cyclist. What should you do?

- ⊙ Overtake very closely
- ⊙ Keep close as you pass
- ⊙ Sound your horn repeatedly
- ⊙ Allow extra room

You are looking for somewhere to park your vehicle. The area is full EXCEPT for spaces marked 'disabled use'. You can

- ⊙ use these spaces when elsewhere is full
- ⊙ park if you stay with your vehicle
- ⊙ use these spaces, disabled or not
- ⊙ not park there unless permitted

A bus lane on your left shows no times of operation. This means it is

- ⊙ not in operation at all
- ⊙ only in operation at peak times
- ⊙ in operation 24 hours a day
- ⊙ only in operation in daylight hours

When being followed by an ambulance showing a flashing blue beacon you should

- ⊙ pull over as soon as safely possible to let it pass
- ⊙ accelerate hard to get away from it
- ⊙ maintain your speed and course
- ⊙ brake harshly and immediately stop in the road

1.7   *Mark **one** answer*

What will reduce the risk of neck injury resulting from a collision?

- ⊙ An air-sprung seat
- ⊙ Anti-lock brakes
- ⊙ A collapsible steering wheel
- ⊙ A properly adjusted head restraint

1.8   *Mark **one** answer*

A red traffic light means

- ⊙ you must stop behind the white stop line
- ⊙ you may go straight on if there is no other traffic
- ⊙ you may turn left if it is safe to do so
- ⊙ you must slow down and prepare to stop if traffic has started to cross

1.9   *Mark **one** answer*

Where would you see a contraflow bus and cycle lane?

- ⊙ On a dual carriageway
- ⊙ On a roundabout
- ⊙ On an urban motorway
- ⊙ On a one-way street

1.10   *Mark **one** answer*

How can driving in an Eco-safe manner help protect the environment?

- ⊙ Through the legal enforcement of speed regulations
- ⊙ By increasing the number of cars on the road
- ⊙ Through increased fuel bills
- ⊙ By reducing exhaust emissions

1.11   *Mark **one** answer*

You are entering an area of roadworks. There is a temporary speed limit displayed. You should

- ⊙ not exceed the speed limit
- ⊙ obey the limit only during rush hour
- ⊙ ignore the displayed limit
- ⊙ obey the limit except at night

1.12   *Mark **one** answer*

There are flashing amber lights under a school warning sign. What action should you take?

- ⊙ Reduce speed until you are clear of the area
- ⊙ Keep up your speed and sound the horn
- ⊙ Increase your speed to clear the area quickly
- ⊙ Wait at the lights until they change to green

As you approach this bridge you should

- ⊙ move into the middle of the road to get a better view
- ⊙ slow down
- ⊙ get over the bridge as quickly as possible
- ⊙ consider using your horn
- ⊙ find another route
- ⊙ beware of pedestrians

You may use front fog lights with headlights ONLY when visibility is reduced to less than

- ⊙ 100 metres (328 feet)
- ⊙ 200 metres (656 feet)
- ⊙ 300 metres (984 feet)
- ⊙ 400 metres (1312 feet)

Congestion Charges apply in the London area. Who of these will NOT have to pay?

- ⊙ A person who lives in the area
- ⊙ A driver making deliveries
- ⊙ A person who is just driving through the area
- ⊙ A driver with no other passengers in the vehicle

What does this sign mean?

- ⊙ Crosswinds
- ⊙ Road noise
- ⊙ Airport
- ⊙ Adverse camber

You arrive at an accident. A motorcyclist is unconscious. Your FIRST priority is the casualty's

- ⊙ breathing
- ⊙ bleeding
- ⊙ broken bones
- ⊙ bruising

You are approaching traffic lights. Red and amber are showing. This means

- ⊙ pass the lights if the road is clear
- ⊙ there is a fault with the lights – take care
- ⊙ wait for the green light before you cross the stop line
- ⊙ the lights are about to change to red

1.19   *Mark two answers*

Which TWO are badly affected if the tyres are under-inflated?

- ⊙ Braking
- ⊙ Steering
- ⊙ Changing gear
- ⊙ Parking

1.20   *Mark one answer*

You are turning left into a side road. What hazards should you be especially aware of?

- ⊙ One way street
- ⊙ Pedestrians
- ⊙ Traffic congestion
- ⊙ Parked vehicles

1.21   *Mark one answer*

What does this sign mean?

- ⊙ Traffic lights out of order
- ⊙ Amber signal out of order
- ⊙ Temporary traffic lights ahead
- ⊙ New traffic lights ahead

1.22   *Mark two answers*

You are driving in town. Ahead of you a bus is at a bus stop. Which TWO of the following should you do?

- ⊙ Be prepared to give way if the bus suddenly moves off
- ⊙ Continue at the same speed but sound your horn as a warning
- ⊙ Watch carefully for the sudden appearance of pedestrians
- ⊙ Pass the bus as quickly as you possibly can

1.23   *Mark one answer*

What is the main hazard the driver of the red car (arrowed) should be aware of?

- ⊙ Glare from the sun may affect the driver's vision
- ⊙ The black car may stop suddenly
- ⊙ The bus may move out into the road
- ⊙ Oncoming vehicles will assume the driver is turning right

1.24

Where are you most likely to be affected by a side wind?

- ⊙ On a narrow country lane
- ⊙ On an open stretch of road
- ⊙ On a busy stretch of road
- ⊙ On a long, straight road

1.25

You are approaching this crossing.
You should

- ⊙ prepare to slow down and stop
- ⊙ stop and wave the pedestrians across
- ⊙ speed up and pass by quickly
- ⊙ continue unless the pedestrians step out

1.26

Your vehicle needs a current MOT certificate. You do not have one. Until you do have one you will not be able to renew your

- ⊙ driving licence
- ⊙ vehicle insurance
- ⊙ road tax disc
- ⊙ vehicle registration document

1.27

You are in the right-hand lane of a dual carriageway. You see signs showing that the right-hand lane is closed 800 yards ahead. You should

- ⊙ keep in that lane until you reach the queue
- ⊙ move to the left immediately
- ⊙ wait and see which lane is moving faster
- ⊙ move to the left in good time

1.28

The police may ask you to produce which three of these documents following an accident?

- ⊙ Vehicle registration document
- ⊙ Driving licence
- ⊙ Theory test certificate
- ⊙ Insurance certificate
- ⊙ MOT test certificate
- ⊙ Road tax disc

1.29

Using rear fog lights in clear daylight will

- ⊙ be useful when towing a trailer
- ⊙ give extra protection
- ⊙ dazzle other drivers
- ⊙ make following drivers keep back

1.30   *Mark **one** answer*

When driving in falling snow you should

- ⊙ brake firmly and quickly
- ⊙ be ready to steer sharply
- ⊙ use sidelights only
- ⊙ brake gently in plenty of time

1.31   *Mark **one** answer*

What is the main hazard you should be aware of when following this cyclist?

- ⊙ The cyclist may move to the left and dismount
- ⊙ The cyclist may swerve out into the road
- ⊙ The contents of the cyclist's carrier may fall onto the road
- ⊙ The cyclist may wish to turn right at the end of the road

1.32   *Mark **one** answer*

You are approaching crossroads. The traffic lights have failed. What should you do?

- ⊙ Brake and stop only for large vehicles
- ⊙ Brake sharply to a stop before looking
- ⊙ Be prepared to brake sharply to a stop
- ⊙ Be prepared to stop for any traffic.

1.33   *Mark **one** answer*

A heavy load on your roof rack will

- ⊙ improve the road holding
- ⊙ reduce the stopping distance
- ⊙ make the steering lighter
- ⊙ reduce stability

1.34   *Mark **one** answer*

You break down on a motorway. You need to call for help. Why may it be better to use an emergency roadside telephone rather than a mobile phone?

- ⊙ It connects you to a local garage
- ⊙ Using a mobile phone will distract other drivers
- ⊙ It allows easy location by the emergency services
- ⊙ Mobile phones do not work on motorways

1.35   *Mark **one** answer*

When joining a motorway you must always

- ⊙ use the hard shoulder
- ⊙ stop at the end of the acceleration lane
- ⊙ come to a stop before joining the motorway
- ⊙ give way to traffic already on the motorway

Revision paper two

2.1   *Mark **one** answer*

The fluid level in your battery is low. What should you top it up with?

- ⊙ Battery acid
- ⊙ Distilled water
- ⊙ Engine oil
- ⊙ Engine coolant

2.2   *Mark **one** answer*

Where would you see this sign?

- ⊙ In the window of a car taking children to school
- ⊙ At the side of the road
- ⊙ At playground areas
- ⊙ On the rear of a school bus or coach

2.3   *Mark **one** answer*

The main cause of brake fade is

- ⊙ the brakes overheating
- ⊙ air in the brake fluid
- ⊙ oil on the brakes
- ⊙ the brakes out of adjustment

2.4   *Mark **one** answer*

What does this sign mean?

- ⊙ Service area 30 miles ahead
- ⊙ Maximum speed 30 mph
- ⊙ Minimum speed 30 mph
- ⊙ Lay-by 30 miles ahead

2.5   *Mark **one** answer*

You are following a slower-moving vehicle on a narrow country road. There is a junction just ahead on the right. What should you do?

- ⊙ Overtake after checking your mirrors and signalling
- ⊙ Stay behind until you are past the junction
- ⊙ Accelerate quickly to pass before the junction
- ⊙ Slow down and prepare to overtake on the left

2.6   *Mark **one** answer*

When leaving your car unattended for a few minutes you should

- ⊙ leave the engine running
- ⊙ switch the engine off but leave the key in
- ⊙ lock it and remove the key
- ⊙ park near a traffic warden

2.7   *Mark **one** answer*

Fuel consumption is at its highest when you are

- ⊙ braking
- ⊙ coasting
- ⊙ accelerating
- ⊙ steering

2.8   *Mark **one** answer*

Ahead of you there is a moving vehicle with a flashing amber beacon. This means it is

- ⊙ slow moving
- ⊙ broken down
- ⊙ a doctor's car
- ⊙ a school crossing patrol

2.9   *Mark **one** answer*

How can you stop a caravan snaking from side to side?

- ⊙ Turn the steering wheel slowly to each side
- ⊙ Accelerate to increase your speed
- ⊙ Stop as quickly as you can
- ⊙ Slow down very gradually

2.10   *Mark **one** answer*

Where would you see these road markings?

- ⊙ At a level crossing
- ⊙ On a motorway slip road
- ⊙ At a pedestrian crossing
- ⊙ On a single-track road

2.11   *Mark **one** answer*

This marking appears on the road just before a

- ⊙ 'no entry' sign
- ⊙ 'give way' sign
- ⊙ 'stop' sign
- ⊙ 'no through road' sign

2.12   *Mark **one** answer*

You start to feel tired while driving. What should you do?

- ⊙ Increase your speed slightly
- ⊙ Decrease your speed slightly
- ⊙ Find a less busy route
- ⊙ Pull over at a safe place to rest

You are following this lorry. You should keep well back from it to

- ⊙ give you a good view of the road ahead
- ⊙ stop following traffic from rushing through the junction
- ⊙ prevent traffic behind you from overtaking
- ⊙ allow you to hurry through the traffic lights if they change

What TWO main hazards should you be aware of when going along this street?

- ⊙ Glare from the sun
- ⊙ Car doors opening suddenly
- ⊙ Lack of road markings
- ⊙ The headlights on parked cars being switched on
- ⊙ Large goods vehicles
- ⊙ Children running out from between vehicles

You meet an obstruction on your side of the road. You should

- ⊙ carry on, you have priority
- ⊙ give way to oncoming traffic
- ⊙ wave oncoming vehicles through
- ⊙ accelerate to get past first

Your vehicle has broken down on an automatic railway level crossing. What should you do FIRST?

- ⊙ Get everyone out of the vehicle and clear of the crossing
- ⊙ Phone the signal operator so that trains can be stopped
- ⊙ Walk along the track to give warning to any approaching trains
- ⊙ Try to push the vehicle clear of the crossing as soon as possible

Which of these signs means the end of a dual carriageway?

⊙   ⊙

⊙   ⊙

2.18
*Mark **one** answer*

You are on a fast, open road in good conditions. For safety, the distance between you and the vehicle in front should be

- ⊙ a two-second time gap
- ⊙ one car length
- ⊙ 2 metres (6 feet 6 inches)
- ⊙ two car lengths

2.19
*Mark **two** answers*

Objects hanging from your interior mirror may

- ⊙ restrict your view
- ⊙ improve your driving
- ⊙ distract your attention
- ⊙ help your concentration

2.20
*Mark **one** answer*

Which arm signal tells you that the car you are following is going to turn left?

⊙   ⊙

⊙   ⊙

2.21
*Mark **three** answers*

Which THREE of the following will affect your stopping distance?

- ⊙ How fast you are going
- ⊙ The tyres on your vehicle
- ⊙ The time of day
- ⊙ The weather
- ⊙ The street lighting

2.22
*Mark **three** answers*

Driving long distances can be tiring. You can prevent this by

- ⊙ stopping every so often for a walk
- ⊙ opening a window for some fresh air
- ⊙ ensuring plenty of refreshment breaks
- ⊙ completing the journey without stopping
- ⊙ eating a large meal before driving

2.23
*Mark **one** answer*

What should you do as you approach this lorry?

- ⊙ Slow down and be prepared to wait
- ⊙ Make the lorry wait for you
- ⊙ Flash your lights at the lorry
- ⊙ Move to the right-hand side of the road

2.24
Mark one answer

When MUST you use dipped headlights during the day?

- ⊙ All the time
- ⊙ Along narrow streets
- ⊙ In poor visibility
- ⊙ When parking

2.25
Mark two answers

What TWO safeguards could you take against fire risk to your vehicle?

- ⊙ Keep water levels above maximum
- ⊙ Carry a fire extinguisher
- ⊙ Avoid driving with a full tank of petrol
- ⊙ Use unleaded petrol
- ⊙ Check out any strong smell of petrol
- ⊙ Use low octane fuel

2.26
Mark one answer

Using front fog lights in clear daylight will

- ⊙ flatten the battery
- ⊙ dazzle other drivers
- ⊙ improve your visibility
- ⊙ increase your awareness

2.27
Mark one answer

Freezing conditions will affect the distance it takes you to come to a stop. You should expect stopping distances to increase by up to

- ⊙ two times
- ⊙ three times
- ⊙ five times
- ⊙ ten times

2.28
Mark one answer

What does this sign mean?

- ⊙ Minimum speed 30 mph
- ⊙ End of maximum speed
- ⊙ End of minimum speed
- ⊙ Maximum speed 30 mph

2.29
Mark one answer

You may only enter a box junction when

- ⊙ there are less than two vehicles in front of you
- ⊙ the traffic lights show green
- ⊙ your exit road is clear
- ⊙ you need to turn left

2.30 *Mark **one** answer*

You are driving on a clear night. There is a steady stream of oncoming traffic. The national speed limit applies. Which lights should you use?

⊙ Full beam headlights

⊙ Sidelights

⊙ Dipped headlights

⊙ Fog lights

2.31 *Mark **one** answer*

When going through a contraflow system on a motorway you should

⊙ ensure that you do not exceed 30 mph

⊙ keep a good distance from the vehicle ahead

⊙ switch lanes to keep the traffic flowing

⊙ stay close to the vehicle ahead to reduce queues

2.32 *Mark **one** answer*

A crawler lane on a motorway is found

⊙ on a steep gradient

⊙ before a service area

⊙ before a junction

⊙ along the hard shoulder

2.33 *Mark **one** answer*

What does this sign tell you?

⊙ No cycling

⊙ Cycle route ahead

⊙ Cycle parking only

⊙ End of cycle route

2.34 *Mark **one** answer*

Which age group of drivers is most likely to be involved in a road accident?

⊙ 17 - 25 year olds

⊙ 36 - 45 year olds

⊙ 46 - 55 year olds

⊙ over 55 year olds

2.35 *Mark **one** answer*

When you approach a bus signalling to move off from a bus stop you should

⊙ get past before it moves

⊙ allow it to pull away, if it is safe to do so

⊙ flash your headlights as you approach

⊙ signal left and wave the bus on

Revision paper three

3.1   *Mark **one** answer*

At an accident you suspect a casualty has back injuries. The area is safe. You should

- offer them a drink
- not move them
- raise their legs
- offer them a cigarette

3.2   *Mark **one** answer*

What does this sign mean?

- With-flow bus and cycle lane
- Contraflow bus and cycle lane
- No buses and cycles allowed
- No waiting for buses and cycles

3.3   *Mark **one** answer*

You are driving in heavy rain. Your steering suddenly becomes very light. You should

- steer towards the side of the road
- apply gentle acceleration
- brake firmly to reduce speed
- ease off the accelerator

3.4   *Mark **one** answer*

You are turning left on a slippery road. The back of your vehicle slides to the right. You should

- brake firmly and not turn the steering wheel
- steer carefully to the left
- steer carefully to the right
- brake firmly and steer to the left

3.5   *Mark **one** answer*

At a pelican crossing, what does a flashing amber light mean?

- You must not move off until the lights stop flashing
- You must give way to pedestrians still on the crossing
- You can move off, even if pedestrians are still on the crossing
- You must stop because the lights are about to change to red

3.6   *Mark **one** answer*

Before you make a U-turn in the road, you should

- give an arm signal as well as using your indicators
- signal so that other drivers can slow down for you
- look over your shoulder for a final check
- select a higher gear than normal

3.7   Mark *three* answers

You arrive at a serious motorcycle accident. The motorcyclist is unconscious and bleeding. Your main priorities should be to

- ⊙ try to stop the bleeding
- ⊙ make a list of witnesses
- ⊙ check the casualty's breathing
- ⊙ take the numbers of the vehicles involved
- ⊙ sweep up any loose debris
- ⊙ check the casualty's airways

3.8   Mark *one* answer

You see these markings on the road. Why are they there?

- ⊙ To show a safe distance between vehicles
- ⊙ To keep the area clear of traffic
- ⊙ To make you aware of your speed
- ⊙ To warn you to change direction

3.9   Mark *one* answer

You have just passed your test. How can you decrease your risk of accidents on the motorway?

- ⊙ By keeping up with the car in front
- ⊙ By never going over 40 mph
- ⊙ By staying only in the left-hand lane
- ⊙ By taking further training

3.10   Mark *one* answer

You are driving at night with full beam headlights on. A vehicle is overtaking you. You should dip your lights

- ⊙ some time after the vehicle has passed you
- ⊙ before the vehicle starts to pass you
- ⊙ only if the other driver dips their headlights
- ⊙ as soon as the vehicle passes you

3.11   Mark *one* answer

A red traffic light means

- ⊙ you should stop unless turning left
- ⊙ stop, if you are able to brake safely
- ⊙ you must stop and wait behind the stop line
- ⊙ proceed with caution

3.12   Mark *three* answers

Which THREE of the following are hazards motorcyclists present in queues of traffic?

- ⊙ Cutting in just in front of you
- ⊙ Riding in single file
- ⊙ Passing very close to you
- ⊙ Riding with their headlight on dipped beam
- ⊙ Filtering between the lanes

*Mark **one** answer*

A newly qualified driver must

- display green 'L' plates
- not exceed 40 mph for 12 months
- be accompanied on a motorway
- have valid motor insurance

3.14 *Mark **one** answer*

You should reduce your speed when driving along this road because

- there is a staggered junction ahead
- there is a low bridge ahead
- there is a change in the road surface
- the road ahead narrows

3.15 *Mark **three** answers*

To avoid an accident when entering a contraflow system, you should

- reduce speed in good time
- switch lanes any time to make progress
- choose an appropriate lane early
- keep the correct separation distance
- increase speed to pass through quickly
- follow other motorists closely to avoid long queues

3.16 *Mark **one** answer*

You see a pedestrian with a white stick and red band. This means that the person is

- physically disabled
- deaf only
- blind only
- deaf and blind

3.17 *Mark **one** answer*

Where would you find these road markings?

- At a railway crossing
- At a junction
- On a motorway
- On a pedestrian crossing

3.18 *Mark **one** answer*

You are testing your suspension. You notice that your vehicle keeps bouncing when you press down on the front wing. What does this mean?

- Worn tyres
- Tyres under-inflated
- Steering wheel not located centrally
- Worn shock absorbers

3.19 *Mark **two** answers*

Which TWO of the following are correct?
When overtaking at night you should

- ⊙ wait until a bend so that you can see the oncoming headlights
- ⊙ sound your horn twice before moving out
- ⊙ be careful because you can see less
- ⊙ beware of bends in the road ahead
- ⊙ put headlights on full beam

3.20 *Mark **one** answer*

In heavy motorway traffic you are being followed closely by the vehicle behind. How can you lower the risk of an accident?

- ⊙ Increase your distance from the vehicle in front
- ⊙ Tap your foot on the brake pedal sharply
- ⊙ Switch on your hazard lights
- ⊙ Move onto the hard shoulder and stop

3.21 *Mark **one** answer*

You are driving along this road. The red van cuts in close in front of you. What should you do?

- ⊙ Accelerate to get closer to the red van
- ⊙ Give a long blast on the horn
- ⊙ Drop back to leave the correct separation distance
- ⊙ Flash your headlights several times

3.22 *Mark **one** answer*

You are driving in town. There is a bus at the bus stop on the other side of the road. Why should you be careful?

- ⊙ The bus may have broken down
- ⊙ Pedestrians may come from behind the bus
- ⊙ The bus may move off suddenly
- ⊙ The bus may remain stationary

3.23 *Mark **one** answer*

You MUST obey signs giving orders. These signs are mostly in

- ⊙ green rectangles
- ⊙ red triangles
- ⊙ blue rectangles
- ⊙ red circles

What does a sign with a brown background show?

⊙ Tourist directions

⊙ Primary roads

⊙ Motorway routes

⊙ Minor routes

Why would you fit a stabiliser before towing a caravan?

⊙ It will help with stability when driving in crosswinds

⊙ It will allow heavy items to be loaded behind the axle

⊙ It will help you to raise and lower the jockey wheel

⊙ It will allow you to tow without the breakaway cable

You are waiting in a traffic queue at night. To avoid dazzling following drivers you should

⊙ apply the handbrake only

⊙ apply the footbrake only

⊙ switch off your headlights

⊙ use both the handbrake and footbrake

Your doctor has given you a course of medicine. Why should you ask how it will affect you?

⊙ Drugs make you a better driver by quickening your reactions

⊙ You will have to let your insurance company know about the medicine

⊙ Some types of medicine can cause your reactions to slow down

⊙ The medicine you take may affect your hearing

Why can it be an advantage for traffic speed to stay constant over a longer distance?

⊙ You will do more stop-start driving

⊙ You will use far more fuel

⊙ You will be able to use more direct routes

⊙ Your overall journey time will normally improve

You are going along a street with parked vehicles on the left-hand side. For which THREE reasons should you keep your speed down?

⊙ So that oncoming traffic can see you more clearly

⊙ You may set off car alarms

⊙ Vehicles may be pulling out

⊙ Drivers' doors may open

⊙ Children may run out from between the vehicles

3.30 Mark *one* answer

You are carrying two 13 year old children and their parents in your car. Who is responsible for seeing that the children wear seat belts?

- ⊙ The children's parents
- ⊙ You, the driver
- ⊙ The front-seat passenger
- ⊙ The children

3.31 Mark *one* answer

You are parking on a two-way road at night. The speed limit is 40 mph. You should park on the

- ⊙ left with parking lights on
- ⊙ left with no lights on
- ⊙ right with parking lights on
- ⊙ right with dipped headlights on

3.32 Mark *one* answer

You are following a long vehicle. It approaches a crossroads and signals left, but moves out to the right. You should

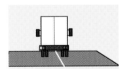

- ⊙ get closer in order to pass it quickly
- ⊙ stay well back and give it room
- ⊙ assume the signal is wrong and it is really turning right
- ⊙ overtake as it starts to slow down

3.33 Mark *one* answer

What is an Emergency Refuge Area on a motorway for?

- ⊙ An area to park in when you want to use a mobile phone
- ⊙ To use in cases of emergency or breakdown
- ⊙ For an emergency recovery vehicle to park in a contra-flow system
- ⊙ To drive in when there is queuing traffic ahead

3.34 Mark *one* answer

What can cause heavy steering?

- ⊙ Driving on ice
- ⊙ Badly worn brakes
- ⊙ Over-inflated tyres
- ⊙ Under-inflated tyres

3.35 Mark *one* answer

It is very windy. You are behind a motorcyclist who is overtaking a high-sided vehicle. What should you do?

- ⊙ Overtake the motorcyclist immediately
- ⊙ Keep well back
- ⊙ Stay level with the motorcyclist
- ⊙ Keep close to the motorcyclist

Revision paper four

4.1   Mark **one** answer

Who is responsible for making sure that a vehicle is not overloaded?

- ⊙ The driver of the vehicle
- ⊙ The owner of the items being carried
- ⊙ The person who loaded the vehicle
- ⊙ The licensing authority

4.2   Mark **two** answers

You are driving along a motorway and become tired. You should

- ⊙ stop at the next service area and rest
- ⊙ leave the motorway at the next exit and rest
- ⊙ increase your speed and turn up the radio volume
- ⊙ close all your windows and set heating to warm
- ⊙ pull up on the hard shoulder and change drivers

4.3   Mark **one** answer

When may you sound the horn?

- ⊙ To give you right of way
- ⊙ To attract a friend's attention
- ⊙ To warn others of your presence
- ⊙ To make slower drivers move over

4.4   Mark **one** answer

You are joining a motorway. Why is it important to make full use of the slip road?

- ⊙ Because there is space available to turn round if you need to
- ⊙ To allow you direct access to the overtaking lanes
- ⊙ To build up a speed similar to traffic on the motorway
- ⊙ Because you can continue on the hard shoulder

4.5   Mark **one** answer

You are driving at night on an unlit road behind another vehicle. You should

- ⊙ flash your headlights
- ⊙ use dipped beam headlights
- ⊙ switch off your headlights
- ⊙ use full beam headlights

4.6   Mark **one** answer

'Red routes' in major cities have been introduced to

- ⊙ raise the speed limits
- ⊙ help the traffic flow
- ⊙ provide better parking
- ⊙ allow lorries to load more freely

4.7   *Mark **one** answer*

Why could keeping the clutch down or selecting neutral for long periods of time be dangerous?

- ⊙ Fuel spillage will occur
- ⊙ Engine damage may be caused
- ⊙ You will have less steering and braking control
- ⊙ It will wear tyres out more quickly

4.8   *Mark **one** answer*

When may you stop on a motorway?

- ⊙ If you have to read a map
- ⊙ When you are tired and need a rest
- ⊙ If your mobile phone rings
- ⊙ In an emergency or breakdown

4.9   *Mark **one** answer*

You are waiting to come out of a side road. Why should you watch carefully for motorcycles?

- ⊙ Motorcycles are usually faster than cars
- ⊙ Police patrols often use motorcycles
- ⊙ Motorcycles are small and hard to see
- ⊙ Motorcycles have right of way

4.10   *Mark **one** answer*

When should you NOT use your horn in a built-up area?

- ⊙ Between 8 pm and 8 am
- ⊙ Between 9 pm and dawn
- ⊙ Between dusk and 8 am
- ⊙ Between 11.30 pm and 7 am

4.11   *Mark **one** answer*

Which of these signs means no motor vehicles?

⊙  ⊙

⊙  ⊙

4.12   *Mark **three** answers*

Which of the following vehicles will use blue flashing beacons?

- ⊙ Motorway maintenance
- ⊙ Bomb disposal
- ⊙ Blood transfusion
- ⊙ Police patrol
- ⊙ Breakdown recovery

27

You have been driving in thick fog which has now cleared. You must switch OFF your rear fog lights because

⊙ they use a lot of power from the battery

⊙ they make your brake lights less clear

⊙ they will cause dazzle in your rear view mirrors

⊙ they may not be properly adjusted

You are approaching a mini-roundabout. The long vehicle in front is signalling left but positioned over to the right. You should

⊙ sound your horn

⊙ overtake on the left

⊙ follow the same course as the lorry

⊙ keep well back

It can help to plan your route before starting a journey. Why should you also plan an alternative route?

⊙ Your original route may be blocked

⊙ Your maps may have different scales

⊙ You may find you have to pay a congestion charge

⊙ Because you may get held up by a tractor

What MUST you do when you see this sign?

⊙ Stop, only if traffic is approaching

⊙ Stop, even if the road is clear

⊙ Stop, only if children are waiting to cross

⊙ Stop, only if a red light is showing

The left-hand pavement is closed due to street repairs. What should you do?

⊙ Watch out for pedestrians walking in the road

⊙ Use your right-hand mirror more often

⊙ Speed up to get past the roadworks quicker

⊙ Position close to the left-hand kerb

Which is a hazard warning line?

⊙   ⊙

⊙   ⊙

4.19 *Mark **one** answer*

What does this sign mean?

- ⊙ No parking
- ⊙ No road markings
- ⊙ No through road
- ⊙ No entry

4.20 *Mark **one** answer*

How can you plan your route before starting a long journey?

- ⊙ Check your vehicle's workshop manual
- ⊙ Ask your local garage
- ⊙ Use a route planner on the internet
- ⊙ Consult your travel agents

4.21 *Mark **one** answer*

You are about to go down a steep hill. To control the speed of your vehicle you should

- ⊙ select a high gear and use the brakes carefully
- ⊙ select a high gear and use the brakes firmly
- ⊙ select a low gear and use the brakes carefully
- ⊙ select a low gear and avoid using the brakes

4.22 *Mark **one** answer*

How would you react to drivers who appear to be inexperienced?

- ⊙ Sound your horn to warn them of your presence
- ⊙ Be patient and prepare for them to react more slowly
- ⊙ Flash your headlights to indicate that it is safe for them to proceed
- ⊙ Overtake them as soon as possible

4.23 *Mark **one** answer*

It is very windy. You are about to overtake a motorcyclist. You should

- ⊙ overtake slowly
- ⊙ allow extra room
- ⊙ sound your horn
- ⊙ keep close as you pass

4.24 *Mark **one** answer*

You are driving on a motorway. The traffic ahead is braking sharply because of an accident. How could you warn traffic behind you?

- ⊙ Briefly use the hazard warning lights
- ⊙ Switch on the hazard warning lights continuously
- ⊙ Briefly use the rear fog lights
- ⊙ Switch on the headlights continuously

You are behind this cyclist. When the traffic lights change, what should you do?

- ◉ Try to move off before the cyclist
- ◉ Allow the cyclist time and room
- ◉ Turn right but give the cyclist room
- ◉ Tap your horn and drive through first

You have broken down on a two-way road. You have a warning triangle. You should place the warning triangle at least how far from your vehicle?

- ◉ 5 metres (16 feet)
- ◉ 25 metres (82 feet)
- ◉ 45 metres (147 feet)
- ◉ 100 metres (328 feet)

At toucan crossings

- ◉ there is no flashing amber light
- ◉ cyclists are not permitted
- ◉ there is a continuously flashing amber beacon
- ◉ pedestrians and cyclists may cross
- ◉ you only stop if someone is waiting to cross

You have stopped at the scene of an accident to give help. Which THREE things should you do?

- ◉ Keep injured people warm and comfortable
- ◉ Keep injured people calm by talking to them reassuringly
- ◉ Keep injured people on the move by walking them around
- ◉ Give injured people a warm drink
- ◉ Make sure that injured people are not left alone

Using a mobile phone when driving is illegal. The chance of you having an accident while using one is

- ◉ two times higher
- ◉ four times higher
- ◉ six times higher
- ◉ ten times higher

4.30 *Mark one answer*

How long will a Statutory Off Road Notification (SORN) last for?

⊙ 12 months

⊙ 24 months

⊙ 3 years

⊙ 10 years

4.31 *Mark one answer*

Which road user has caused a hazard?

⊙ The parked car (arrowed A)

⊙ The pedestrian waiting to cross (arrowed B)

⊙ The moving car (arrowed C)

⊙ The car turning (arrowed D)

4.32 *Mark two answers*

How can you tell if you are driving on ice?

⊙ The tyres make a rumbling noise

⊙ The tyres make hardly any noise

⊙ The steering becomes heavier

⊙ The steering becomes lighter

4.33 *Mark one answer*

You are travelling on a well-lit road at night in a built-up area. By using dipped headlights you will be able to

⊙ see further along the road

⊙ go at a much faster speed

⊙ switch to main beam quickly

⊙ be easily seen by others

4.34 *Mark one answer*

When may you reverse from a side road into a main road?

⊙ Only if both roads are clear of traffic

⊙ Not at any time

⊙ At any time

⊙ Only if the main road is clear of traffic

4.35 *Mark one answer*

You are approaching a busy junction. There are several lanes with road markings. At the last moment you realise that you are in the wrong lane. You should

⊙ continue in that lane

⊙ force your way across

⊙ stop until the area has cleared

⊙ use clear arm signals to cut across

Revision paper five

5.1 Mark **one** answer

When may you drive a motor car in this bus lane?

- ⊙ Outside its hours of operation
- ⊙ To get to the front of a traffic queue
- ⊙ You may not use it at any time
- ⊙ To overtake slow-moving traffic

5.2 Mark **one** answer

What is the right-hand lane used for on a three-lane motorway?

- ⊙ Emergency vehicles only
- ⊙ Overtaking
- ⊙ Vehicles towing trailers
- ⊙ Coaches only

5.3 Mark **one** answer

Why are mirrors often slightly curved (convex)?

- ⊙ They give a wider field of vision
- ⊙ They totally cover blind spots
- ⊙ They make it easier to judge the speed of following traffic
- ⊙ They make following traffic look bigger

5.4 Mark **one** answer

A single carriageway road has this sign. What is the maximum permitted speed for a car towing a trailer?

- ⊙ 30 mph
- ⊙ 40 mph
- ⊙ 50 mph
- ⊙ 60 mph

5.5 Mark **one** answer

You are travelling in very heavy rain. Your overall stopping distance is likely to be

- ⊙ doubled
- ⊙ halved
- ⊙ up to ten times greater
- ⊙ no different

5.6 Mark **two** answers

Driving with under-inflated tyres can affect

- ⊙ engine temperature
- ⊙ fuel consumption
- ⊙ braking
- ⊙ oil pressure

5.7 Mark **one** answer

You are driving on a wet road. You have to stop your vehicle in an emergency. You should

- ⊙ apply the handbrake and footbrake together
- ⊙ keep both hands on the wheel
- ⊙ select reverse gear
- ⊙ give an arm signal

5.8 Mark **one** answer

What is the legal minimum insurance cover you must have to drive on public roads?

- ⊙ Third party, fire and theft
- ⊙ Comprehensive
- ⊙ Third party only
- ⊙ Personal injury cover

5.9 Mark **one** answer

What is the meaning of this sign?

- ⊙ Local speed limit applies
- ⊙ No waiting on the carriageway
- ⊙ National speed limit applies
- ⊙ No entry to vehicular traffic

5.10 Mark **one** answer

You are following a large lorry on a wet road. Spray makes it difficult to see. You should

- ⊙ drop back until you can see better
- ⊙ put your headlights on full beam
- ⊙ keep close to the lorry, away from the spray
- ⊙ speed up and overtake quickly

5.11 Mark **one** answer

On a motorway what is used to reduce traffic bunching?

- ⊙ Variable speed limits
- ⊙ Contraflow systems
- ⊙ National speed limits
- ⊙ Lane closures

5.12 Mark **one** answer

You are waiting to emerge left from a minor road. A large vehicle is approaching from the right. You have time to turn, but you should wait. Why?

- ⊙ The large vehicle can easily hide an overtaking vehicle
- ⊙ The large vehicle can turn suddenly
- ⊙ The large vehicle is difficult to steer in a straight line
- ⊙ The large vehicle can easily hide vehicles from the left

5.13
Mark **one** answer

What does this sign mean?

- ⊙ Wait at the barriers
- ⊙ Wait at the crossroads
- ⊙ Give way to trams
- ⊙ Give way to farm vehicles

5.14
Mark **one** answer

What does this sign mean?

- ⊙ End of restricted speed area
- ⊙ End of restricted parking area
- ⊙ End of clearway
- ⊙ End of cycle route

5.15
Mark **one** answer

Traffic calming measures are used to

- ⊙ stop road rage
- ⊙ help overtaking
- ⊙ slow traffic down
- ⊙ help parking

5.16
Mark **one** answer

On a motorway this sign means

- ⊙ move over onto the hard shoulder
- ⊙ overtaking on the left only
- ⊙ leave the motorway at the next exit
- ⊙ move to the lane on your left

5.17
Mark **one** answer

You are going through a congested tunnel and have to stop. What should you do?

- ⊙ Pull up very close to the vehicle in front to save space
- ⊙ Ignore any message signs as they are never up to date
- ⊙ Keep a safe distance from the vehicle in front
- ⊙ Make a U-turn and find another route

5.18
Mark **one** answer

Which instrument panel warning light would show that headlights are on full beam?

⊙   ⊙

⊙   ⊙

5.19 *Mark **one** answer*

The road outside this school is marked with yellow zigzag lines. What do these lines mean?

- ⊙ You may park on the lines when dropping off schoolchildren
- ⊙ You may park on the lines when picking schoolchildren up
- ⊙ You must not wait or park your vehicle here at all
- ⊙ You must stay with your vehicle if you park here

5.20 *Mark **one** answer*

You are waiting at a T-junction. A vehicle is coming from the right with the left signal flashing. What should you do?

- ⊙ Move out and accelerate hard
- ⊙ Wait until the vehicle starts to turn in
- ⊙ Pull out before the vehicle reaches the junction
- ⊙ Move out slowly

5.21 *Mark **one** answer*

You are following a cyclist. You wish to turn left just ahead. You should

- ⊙ overtake the cyclist before the junction
- ⊙ pull alongside the cyclist and stay level until after the junction
- ⊙ hold back until the cyclist has passed the junction
- ⊙ go around the cyclist on the junction

5.22 *Mark **one** answer*

Rapid acceleration and heavy braking can lead to

- ⊙ reduced pollution
- ⊙ increased fuel consumption
- ⊙ reduced exhaust emissions
- ⊙ increased road safety

5.23 *Mark **one** answer*

You are in a one-way street and want to turn right. You should position yourself

- ⊙ in the right-hand lane
- ⊙ in the left-hand lane
- ⊙ in either lane, depending on the traffic
- ⊙ just left of the centre line

*Mark **one** answer*

Traffic signs giving orders are generally which shape?

*Mark **one** answer*

Which sign means that there may be people walking along the road?

*Mark **one** answer*

After an accident, someone is unconscious in their vehicle. When should you call the emergency services?

- ⊙ Only as a last resort
- ⊙ As soon as possible
- ⊙ After you have woken them up
- ⊙ After checking for broken bones

*Mark **one** answer*

If your motorway journey seems boring and you feel drowsy while driving, you should

- ⊙ open a window and drive to the next service area
- ⊙ stop on the hard shoulder for a sleep
- ⊙ speed up to arrive at your destination sooner
- ⊙ slow down and let other drivers overtake

*Mark **one** answer*

You are driving along this road. The driver on the left is reversing from a driveway. You should

- ⊙ move to the opposite side of the road
- ⊙ drive through as you have priority
- ⊙ sound your horn and be prepared to stop
- ⊙ speed up and drive through quickly

*Mark **one** answer*

Planning your route before setting out can be helpful. How can you do this?

- ⊙ Look in a motoring magazine
- ⊙ Only visit places you know
- ⊙ Try to travel at busy times
- ⊙ Print or write down the route

5.30 *Mark **one** answer*

You are driving along a wet road. How can you tell if your vehicle's tyres are losing their grip on the surface?

- ⊙ The engine will stall
- ⊙ The steering will feel very heavy
- ⊙ The engine noise will increase
- ⊙ The steering will feel very light

5.31 *Mark **one** answer*

You are following a motorcyclist on an uneven road. You should

- ⊙ allow less room so you can be seen in their mirrors
- ⊙ overtake immediately
- ⊙ allow extra room in case they swerve to avoid potholes
- ⊙ allow the same room as normal because road surfaces do not affect motorcyclists

5.32 *Mark **one** answer*

A roof rack fitted to your car will

- ⊙ reduce fuel consumption
- ⊙ improve the road handling
- ⊙ make your car go faster
- ⊙ increase fuel consumption

5.33 *Mark **one** answer*

You are following a vehicle at a safe distance on a wet road. Another driver overtakes you and pulls into the gap you have left. What should you do?

- ⊙ Flash your headlights as a warning
- ⊙ Try to overtake safely as soon as you can
- ⊙ Drop back to regain a safe distance
- ⊙ Stay close to the other vehicle until it moves on

5.34 *Mark **three** answers*

Which THREE result from drinking alcohol?

- ⊙ Less control
- ⊙ A false sense of confidence
- ⊙ Faster reactions
- ⊙ Poor judgement of speed
- ⊙ Greater awareness of danger

5.35 *Mark **one** answer*

You are towing a caravan along a motorway. The caravan begins to swerve from side to side. What should you do?

- ⊙ Ease off the accelerator slowly
- ⊙ Steer sharply from side to side
- ⊙ Do an emergency stop
- ⊙ Speed up very quickly

Revision paper six

6.1   *Mark **one** answer*

You will feel the effects of engine braking when you

- ◉ only use the handbrake
- ◉ only use neutral
- ◉ change to a lower gear
- ◉ change to a higher gear

6.2   *Mark **one** answer*

Why is it particularly important to carry out a check on your vehicle before making a long motorway journey?

- ◉ You will have to do more harsh braking on motorways
- ◉ Motorway service stations do not deal with breakdowns
- ◉ The road surface will wear down the tyres faster
- ◉ Continuous high speeds may increase the risk of your vehicle breaking down

6.3   *Mark **one** answer*

When going straight ahead at a roundabout you should

- ◉ indicate left before leaving the roundabout
- ◉ not indicate at any time
- ◉ indicate right when approaching the roundabout
- ◉ indicate left when approaching the roundabout

6.4   *Mark **one** answer*

There is a slow-moving motorcyclist ahead of you. You are unsure what the rider is going to do. You should

- ◉ pass on the left
- ◉ pass on the right
- ◉ stay behind
- ◉ move closer

6.5   *Mark **two** answers*

You have stopped at a pelican crossing. A disabled person is crossing slowly in front of you. The lights have now changed to green. You should

- ◉ allow the person to cross
- ◉ drive in front of the person
- ◉ drive behind the person
- ◉ sound your horn
- ◉ be patient
- ◉ edge forward slowly

6.6   *Mark **one** answer*

A toucan crossing is different from other crossings because

- ◉ moped riders can use it
- ◉ it is controlled by a traffic warden
- ◉ it is controlled by two flashing lights
- ◉ cyclists can use it

6.7 *Mark **one** answer*

You are parked in a busy high street. What is the safest way to turn your vehicle around so you can go the opposite way?

- ⊙ Find a quiet side road to turn round in
- ⊙ Drive into a side road and reverse into the main road
- ⊙ Get someone to stop the traffic
- ⊙ Do a U-turn

6.8 *Mark **one** answer*

Why do MOT tests include a strict exhaust emission test?

- ⊙ To recover the cost of expensive garage equipment
- ⊙ To help protect the environment against pollution
- ⊙ To discover which fuel supplier is used the most
- ⊙ To make sure diesel and petrol engines emit the same fumes

6.9 *Mark **one** answer*

What does this sign mean?

- ⊙ Multi-exit roundabout
- ⊙ Risk of ice
- ⊙ Six roads converge
- ⊙ Place of historical interest

6.10 *Mark **one** answer*

At a busy unmarked crossroads, which of the following has priority?

- ⊙ Vehicles going straight ahead
- ⊙ Vehicles turning right
- ⊙ None of the vehicles
- ⊙ The vehicles that arrived first

6.11 *Mark **one** answer*

You are travelling along the left-hand lane of a three-lane motorway. Traffic is joining from a slip road. You should

- ⊙ race the other vehicles
- ⊙ move to another lane
- ⊙ maintain a steady speed
- ⊙ switch on your hazard flashers

6.12 *Mark **one** answer*

What is the reason for the yellow criss-cross lines painted on the road here?

- ⊙ To mark out an area for trams only
- ⊙ To prevent queuing traffic from blocking the junction on the left
- ⊙ To mark the entrance lane to a car park
- ⊙ To warn you of the tram lines crossing the road

6.13
*Mark **one** answer*

To avoid spillage after refuelling, you should make sure that

- ⊙ your tank is only three quarters full
- ⊙ you have used a locking filler cap
- ⊙ you check your fuel gauge is working
- ⊙ your filler cap is securely fastened

6.14
*Mark **one** answer*

Which sign means NO motor vehicles allowed?

⊙   ⊙

⊙   ⊙

6.15
*Mark **three** answers*

Excessive or uneven tyre wear can be caused by faults in which THREE of the following?

- ⊙ The gearbox
- ⊙ The braking system
- ⊙ The accelerator
- ⊙ The exhaust system
- ⊙ Wheel alignment
- ⊙ The suspension

6.16
*Mark **one** answer*

When may you wait in a box junction?

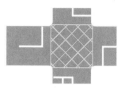

- ⊙ When you are stationary in a queue of traffic
- ⊙ When approaching a pelican crossing
- ⊙ When approaching a zebra crossing
- ⊙ When oncoming traffic prevents you turning right

6.17
*Mark **one** answer*

You arrive at an accident where someone is suffering from severe burns. You should

- ⊙ apply lotions to the injury
- ⊙ burst any blisters
- ⊙ remove anything stuck to the burns
- ⊙ douse the burns with cool liquid

6.18
*Mark **one** answer*

Your vehicle is fitted with a navigation system. How should you avoid letting this distract you while driving?

- ⊙ Keep going and input your destination into the system
- ⊙ Keep going as the system will adjust to your route
- ⊙ Stop immediately to view and use the system
- ⊙ Stop in a safe place before using the system

6.19 *Mark **one** answer*

You are taking drugs that are likely to affect your driving. What should you do?

⊙ Seek medical advice before driving

⊙ Limit your driving to essential journeys

⊙ Only drive if accompanied by a full licence-holder

⊙ Drive only for short distances

6.20 *Mark **one** answer*

Before starting a journey it is wise to plan your route. How can you do this?

⊙ Look at a map

⊙ Contact your local garage

⊙ Look in your vehicle handbook

⊙ Check your vehicle registration document

6.21 *Mark **one** answer*

The driver of the car in front is giving this arm signal. What does it mean?

⊙ The driver is slowing down

⊙ The driver intends to turn right

⊙ The driver wishes to overtake

⊙ The driver intends to turn left

6.22 *Mark **one** answer*

What does this sign mean?

⊙ Through traffic to use left lane

⊙ Right-hand lane T-junction only

⊙ Right-hand lane closed ahead

⊙ 11 tonne weight limit

6.23 *Mark **one** answer*

You have driven through a flood. What is the first thing you should do?

⊙ Stop and check the tyres

⊙ Stop and dry the brakes

⊙ Check your exhaust

⊙ Test your brakes

6.24 *Mark **one** answer*

You intend to turn right into a side road. Just before turning you should check for motorcyclists who might be

⊙ overtaking on your left

⊙ following you closely

⊙ emerging from the side road

⊙ overtaking on your right

6.25 *Mark **one** answer*

On the motorway, the hard shoulder should be used

⊙ to answer a mobile phone

⊙ when an emergency arises

⊙ for a short rest when tired

⊙ to check a road atlas

6.26 *Mark **one** answer*

This yellow sign on a vehicle indicates this is

⊙ a broken-down vehicle

⊙ a school bus

⊙ an ice cream van

⊙ a private ambulance

6.27 *Mark **one** answer*

You are driving towards this level crossing. What would be the first warning of an approaching train?

⊙ Both half barriers down

⊙ A steady amber light

⊙ One half barrier down

⊙ Twin flashing red lights

6.28 *Mark **one** answer*

Unbalanced wheels on a car may cause

⊙ the steering to pull to one side

⊙ the steering to vibrate

⊙ the brakes to fail

⊙ the tyres to deflate

6.29 *Mark **one** answer*

You are on a good, dry, road surface and your vehicle has good brakes and tyres. What is the typical overall stopping distance at 40 mph?

⊙ 23 metres (75 feet)

⊙ 36 metres (120 feet)

⊙ 53 metres (175 feet)

⊙ 96 metres (315 feet)

6.30 *Mark **one** answer*

Which of these is LEAST likely to be affected by crosswinds?

⊙ Cyclists

⊙ Motorcyclists

⊙ High-sided vehicles

⊙ Cars

6.31
*Mark **one** answer*

You are driving in traffic at the speed limit for the road. The driver behind is trying to overtake. You should

⊙ move closer to the car ahead, so the driver behind has no room to overtake

⊙ wave the driver behind to overtake when it is safe

⊙ keep a steady course and allow the driver behind to overtake

⊙ accelerate to get away from the driver behind

6.32
*Mark **one** answer*

Are passengers allowed to ride in a caravan that is being towed?

⊙ Yes, if they are over fourteen

⊙ No, not at any time

⊙ Only if all the seats in the towing vehicle are full

⊙ Only if a stabiliser is fitted

6.33
*Mark **one** answer*

You have been convicted of driving whilst unfit through drink or drugs. You will find this is likely to cause the cost of one of the following to rise considerably. Which one?

⊙ Road fund licence

⊙ Insurance premiums

⊙ Vehicle test certificate

⊙ Driving licence

6.34
*Mark **one** answer*

Why is passing a lorry more risky than passing a car?

⊙ Lorries are longer than cars

⊙ Lorries may suddenly pull up

⊙ The brakes of lorries are not as good

⊙ Lorries climb hills more slowly

6.35
*Mark **one** answer*

A Statutory Off Road Notification (SORN) will last

⊙ for the life of the vehicle

⊙ for as long as you own the vehicle

⊙ for 12 months only

⊙ until the vehicle warranty expires

Revision paper seven

To help keep your car secure you could join a

- ⊙ vehicle breakdown organisation
- ⊙ vehicle watch scheme
- ⊙ advanced driver's scheme
- ⊙ car maintenance class

You are waiting to emerge at a junction. Your view is restricted by parked vehicles. What can help you to see traffic on the road you are joining?

- ⊙ Looking for traffic behind you
- ⊙ Reflections of traffic in shop windows
- ⊙ Making eye contact with other road users
- ⊙ Checking for traffic in your interior mirror

You are approaching traffic lights that have been on green for some time. You should

- ⊙ accelerate hard
- ⊙ maintain your speed
- ⊙ be ready to stop
- ⊙ brake hard

After a breakdown you need to rejoin the main carriageway of a motorway from the hard shoulder. You should

- ⊙ move out onto the carriageway then build up your speed
- ⊙ move out onto the carriageway using your hazard lights
- ⊙ gain speed on the hard shoulder before moving out onto the carriageway
- ⊙ wait on the hard shoulder until someone flashes their headlights at you

Which type of vehicle does this sign apply to?

- ⊙ Wide vehicles
- ⊙ Long vehicles
- ⊙ High vehicles
- ⊙ Heavy vehicles

You are on a motorway. There are red flashing lights above every lane. You must

- ⊙ pull onto the hard shoulder
- ⊙ slow down and watch for further signals
- ⊙ leave at the next exit
- ⊙ stop and wait

7.7 *Mark **three** answers*

You have third party insurance. What does this cover?

- ⊙ Damage to your own vehicle
- ⊙ Damage to your vehicle by fire
- ⊙ Injury to another person
- ⊙ Damage to someone's property
- ⊙ Damage to other vehicles
- ⊙ Injury to yourself

7.8 *Mark **one** answer*

What is the main hazard shown in this picture?

- ⊙ Vehicles turning right
- ⊙ Vehicles doing U-turns
- ⊙ The cyclist crossing the road
- ⊙ Parked cars around the corner

7.9 *Mark **one** answer*

How can you use your vehicle's engine as a brake?

- ⊙ By changing to a lower gear
- ⊙ By selecting reverse gear
- ⊙ By changing to a higher gear
- ⊙ By selecting neutral gear

7.10 *Mark **one** answer*

What does the solid white line at the side of the road indicate?

- ⊙ Traffic lights ahead
- ⊙ Edge of the carriageway
- ⊙ Footpath on the left
- ⊙ Cycle path

7.11 *Mark **one** answer*

On a foggy day you unavoidably have to park your car on the road. You should

- ⊙ leave your headlights on
- ⊙ leave your fog lights on
- ⊙ leave your sidelights on
- ⊙ leave your hazard lights on

7.12 *Mark **one** answer*

As well as planning your route before starting a journey, you should also plan an alternative route. Why is this?

- ⊙ To let another driver overtake
- ⊙ Your first route may be blocked
- ⊙ To avoid a railway level crossing
- ⊙ In case you have to avoid emergency vehicles

What should you do when leaving
your vehicle?

- ⊙ Put valuable documents under the seats
- ⊙ Remove all valuables
- ⊙ Cover valuables with a blanket
- ⊙ Leave the interior light on

You must NOT sound your horn

- ⊙ between 10 pm and 6 am in a
  built-up area
- ⊙ at any time in a built-up area
- ⊙ between 11.30 pm and 7 am in a
  built-up area
- ⊙ between 11.30 pm and 6 am on
  any road

What does this sign mean?

- ⊙ Contraflow pedal cycle lane
- ⊙ With-flow pedal cycle lane
- ⊙ Pedal cycles and buses only
- ⊙ No pedal cycles or buses

As a provisional licence holder, you must
not drive a motor car

- ⊙ at more than 40 mph
- ⊙ on your own
- ⊙ on the motorway
- ⊙ under the age of 18 years at night
- ⊙ with passengers in the rear seats

The driver of this car is giving an arm signal.
What are they about to do?

- ⊙ Turn to the right
- ⊙ Turn to the left
- ⊙ Go straight ahead
- ⊙ Let pedestrians cross

You are travelling along a motorway.
You see this sign. You should

- ⊙ leave the motorway at the next exit
- ⊙ turn left immediately
- ⊙ change lane
- ⊙ move onto the hard shoulder

7.19   *Mark **one** answer*

Which of these signs means turn left ahead?

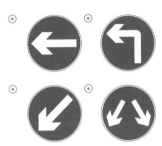

7.20   *Mark **two** answers*

You are driving along a country road. A horse and rider are approaching. What should you do?

⊙ Increase your speed
⊙ Sound your horn
⊙ Flash your headlights
⊙ Drive slowly past
⊙ Give plenty of room
⊙ Rev your engine

7.21   *Mark **one** answer*

What does this sign mean?

⊙ Crossroads
⊙ Level crossing with gate
⊙ Level crossing without gate
⊙ Ahead only

7.22   *Mark **one** answer*

You are turning left into a side road. Pedestrians are crossing the road near the junction. You must

⊙ wave them on
⊙ sound your horn
⊙ switch on your hazard lights
⊙ wait for them to cross

7.23   *Mark **one** answer*

Before overtaking a large vehicle you should keep well back. Why is this?

⊙ To give acceleration space to overtake quickly on blind bends
⊙ To get the best view of the road ahead
⊙ To leave a gap in case the vehicle stops and rolls back
⊙ To offer other drivers a safe gap if they want to overtake you

---

7.24   *Mark **one** answer*

At an accident a small child is not breathing. When giving mouth to mouth you should breathe

⊙ sharply
⊙ gently
⊙ heavily
⊙ rapidly

47

You wish to tow a trailer. Where would you find the maximum noseweight of your vehicle's tow ball?

- ⊙ In the vehicle handbook
- ⊙ In The Highway Code
- ⊙ In your vehicle registration certificate
- ⊙ In your licence documents

You want to turn right at a box junction. There is oncoming traffic. You should

- ⊙ wait in the box junction if your exit is clear
- ⊙ wait before the junction until it is clear of all traffic
- ⊙ drive on, you cannot turn right at a box junction
- ⊙ drive slowly into the box junction when signalled by oncoming traffic

You are on a good, dry road surface. Your vehicle has good brakes and tyres. What is the BRAKING distance at 50 mph?

- ⊙ 38 metres (125 feet)
- ⊙ 14 metres (46 feet)
- ⊙ 24 metres (79 feet)
- ⊙ 55 metres (180 feet)

You are following a long vehicle approaching a crossroads. The driver signals right but moves close to the left-hand kerb. What should you do?

- ⊙ Warn the driver of the wrong signal
- ⊙ Wait behind the long vehicle
- ⊙ Report the driver to the police
- ⊙ Overtake on the right-hand side

Why are vehicles fitted with rear fog lights?

- ⊙ To be seen when driving at high speed
- ⊙ To use if broken down in a dangerous position
- ⊙ To make them more visible in thick fog
- ⊙ To warn drivers following closely to drop back

You are following a car driven by an elderly driver. You should

- ⊙ expect the driver to drive badly
- ⊙ flash your lights and overtake
- ⊙ be aware that the driver's reactions may not be as fast as yours
- ⊙ stay very close behind but be careful

7.31   *Mark **one** answer*

You stop for pedestrians waiting to cross at a zebra crossing. They do not start to cross. What should you do?

- ⊙ Be patient and wait
- ⊙ Sound your horn
- ⊙ Carry on
- ⊙ Wave them to cross

7.32   *Mark **one** answer*

You are at a road junction, turning into a minor road. There are pedestrians crossing the minor road. You should

- ⊙ stop and wave the pedestrians across
- ⊙ sound your horn to let the pedestrians know that you are there
- ⊙ give way to the pedestrians who are already crossing
- ⊙ carry on; the pedestrians should give way to you

7.33   *Mark **one** answer*

On a clearway you must not stop

- ⊙ at any time
- ⊙ when it is busy
- ⊙ in the rush hour
- ⊙ during daylight hours

7.34   *Mark **two** answers*

There has been an accident. The driver is suffering from shock. You should

- ⊙ give them a drink
- ⊙ reassure them
- ⊙ not leave them alone
- ⊙ offer them a cigarette
- ⊙ ask who caused the accident

7.35   *Mark **one** answer*

What does this sign tell you?

- ⊙ That it is a no-through road
- ⊙ End of traffic calming zone
- ⊙ Free parking zone ends
- ⊙ No waiting zone ends

Answers **Paper one**

1.1 Check the label to see if the medicine will affect your driving

1.2 Give the cyclist plenty of room

1.3 Allow extra room

1.4 not park there unless permitted

1.5 in operation 24 hours a day

1.6 pull over as soon as safely possible to let it pass

1.7 A properly adjusted head restraint

1.8 you must stop behind the white stop line

1.9 On a one-way street

1.10 By reducing exhaust emissions

1.11 not exceed the speed limit

1.12 Reduce speed until you are clear of the area

1.13 slow down

consider using your horn

beware of pedestrians

1.14 100 metres (328 feet)

1.15 A person who lives in the area

1.16 Crosswinds

1.17 breathing

1.18 wait for the green light before you cross the stop line

1.19 Braking

Steering

1.20 Pedestrians

1.21 Traffic lights out of order

1.22 Be prepared to give way if the bus suddenly moves off

Watch carefully for the sudden appearance of pedestrians

1.23 The bus may move out into the road

1.24 On an open stretch of road

1.25 prepare to slow down and stop

1.26 road tax disc

1.27 move to the left in good time

1.28 Driving licence

Insurance certificate

MOT test certificate

1.29 dazzle other drivers

1.30 brake gently in plenty of time

1.31 The cyclist may swerve out into the road

1.32 Be prepared to stop for any traffic.

1.33 reduce stability

1.34 It allows easy location by the emergency services

1.35 give way to traffic already on the motorway

Answers **Paper two**

2.1 Distilled water

2.2 On the rear of a school bus or coach

2.3 the brakes overheating

2.4 Minimum speed 30 mph

2.5 Stay behind until you are past the junction

2.6 lock it and remove the key

2.7 accelerating

2.8 slow moving

2.9 Slow down very gradually

2.10 On a motorway slip road

2.11 'give way' sign

2.12 Pull over at a safe place to rest

2.13 give you a good view of the road ahead

2.14 Car doors opening suddenly

Children running out from between vehicles

2.15 give way to oncoming traffic

2.16 Get everyone out of the vehicle and clear of the crossing

2.17

2.18 a two-second time gap

2.19 restrict your view

distract your attention

2.20

2.21 How fast you are going

The tyres on your vehicle

The weather

2.22 stopping every so often for a walk

opening a window for some fresh air

ensuring plenty of refreshment breaks

2.23 Slow down and be prepared to wait

2.24 In poor visibility

2.25 Carry a fire extinguisher

Check out any strong smell of petrol

2.26 dazzle other drivers

2.27 ten times

2.28 End of minimum speed

2.29 your exit road is clear

2.30 Dipped headlights

2.31 keep a good distance from the vehicle ahead

2.32 on a steep gradient

2.33 Cycle route ahead

2.34 17 - 25 year olds

2.35 allow it to pull away, if it is safe to do so

Answers **Paper three**

3.1 not move them

3.2 With-flow bus and cycle lane

3.3 ease off the accelerator

3.4 steer carefully to the right

3.5 You must give way to pedestrians still on the crossing

3.6 look over your shoulder for a final check

3.7 try to stop the bleeding

check the casualty's breathing

check the casualty's airways

3.8 To make you aware of your speed

3.9 By taking further training

3.10 as soon as the vehicle passes you

3.11 you must stop and wait behind the stop line

3.12 Cutting in just in front of you

Passing very close to you

Filtering between the lanes

3.13 have valid motor insurance

3.14 there is a staggered junction ahead

3.15 reduce speed in good time

choose an appropriate lane early

keep the correct separation distance

3.16 deaf and blind

3.17 At a junction

3.18 Worn shock absorbers

3.19 be careful because you can see less

beware of bends in the road ahead

3.20 Increase your distance from the vehicle in front

3.21 Drop back to leave the correct separation distance

3.22 Pedestrians may come from behind the bus

3.23 red circles

3.24 Tourist directions

3.25 It will help with stability when driving in crosswinds

3.26 apply the handbrake only

3.27 Some types of medicine can cause your reactions to slow down

3.28 Your overall journey time will normally improve

3.29 Vehicles may be pulling out

Drivers' doors may open

Children may run out from between the vehicles

3.30 You, the driver

3.31 left with parking lights on

3.32 stay well back and give it room

3.33 To use in cases of emergency or breakdown

3.34 Under-inflated tyres

3.35 Keep well back

Answers **Paper four**

4.1 The driver of the vehicle

4.2 stop at the next service area and rest

leave the motorway at the next exit and rest

4.3 To warn others of your presence

4.4 To build up a speed similar to traffic on the motorway

4.5 use dipped beam headlights

4.6 help the traffic flow

4.7 You will have less steering and braking control

4.8 In an emergency or breakdown

4.9 Motorcycles are small and hard to see

4.10 Between 11.30 pm and 7 am

4.11

4.12 Bomb disposal

Blood transfusion

Police patrol

4.13 they make your brake lights less clear

4.14 keep well back

4.15 Your original route may be blocked

4.16 Stop, even if the road is clear

4.17 Watch out for pedestrians walking in the road

4.18

4.19 No entry

4.20 Use a route planner on the internet

4.21 select a low gear and use the brakes carefully

4.22 Be patient and prepare for them to react more slowly

4.23 allow extra room

4.24 Briefly use the hazard warning lights

4.25 Allow the cyclist time and room

4.26 45 metres (147 feet)

4.27 there is no flashing amber light

pedestrians and cyclists may cross

4.28 Keep injured people warm and comfortable

Keep injured people calm by talking to them reassuringly

Make sure that injured people are not left alone

4.29 four times higher

4.30 12 months

4.31 The parked car (arrowed A)

4.32 The tyres make hardly any noise

The steering becomes lighter

4.33 be easily seen by others

4.34 Not at any time

4.35 continue in that lane

Answers **Paper five**

5.1 Outside its hours of operation

5.2 Overtaking

5.3 They give a wider field of vision

5.4 50 mph

5.5 doubled

5.6 fuel consumption

braking

5.7 keep both hands on the wheel

5.8 Third party only

5.9 National speed limit applies

5.10 drop back until you can see better

5.11 Variable speed limits

5.12 The large vehicle can easily hide an overtaking vehicle

5.13 Give way to trams

5.14 End of restricted parking area

5.15 slow traffic down

5.16 move to the lane on your left

5.17 Keep a safe distance from the vehicle in front

5.18

5.19 You must not wait or park your vehicle here at all

5.20 Wait until the vehicle starts to turn in

5.21 hold back until the cyclist has passed the junction

5.22 increased fuel consumption

5.23 in the right-hand lane

5.24

5.25

5.26 As soon as possible

5.27 open a window and drive to the next service area

5.28 sound your horn and be prepared to stop

5.29 a motoring organisation

5.30 The steering will feel very light

5.31 Print or write down the route

5.32 increase fuel consumption

5.33 Drop back to regain a safe distance

5.34 Less control

A false sense of confidence

Poor judgement of speed

5.35 Ease off the accelerator slowly

Answers **Paper six**

6.1 change to a lower gear

6.2 Continuous high speeds may increase the risk of your vehicle breaking down

6.3 indicate left before leaving the roundabout

6.4 stay behind

6.5 allow the person to cross

be patient

6.6 cyclists can use it

6.7 Find a quiet side road to turn round in

6.8 To help protect the environment against pollution

6.9 Risk of ice

6.10 None of the vehicles

6.11 move to another lane

6.12 To prevent queuing traffic from blocking the junction on the left

6.13 your filler cap is securely fastened

6.14

6.15 The braking system

Wheel alignment

The suspension

6.16 When oncoming traffic prevents you turning right

6.17 douse the burns with cool liquid

6.18 Stop in a safe place before using the system

6.19 Seek medical advice before driving

6.20 Look at a map

6.21 The driver intends to turn left

6.22 Right-hand lane closed ahead

6.23 Test your brakes

6.24 overtaking on your right

6.25 when an emergency arises

6.26 a school bus

6.27 A steady amber light

6.28 the steering to vibrate

6.29	36 metres (120 feet)
6.30	Cars
6.31	keep a steady course and allow the driver behind to overtake
6.32	No, not at any time
6.33	Insurance premiums
6.34	Lorries are longer than cars
6.35	for 12 months only

Answers **Paper seven**

7.1	vehicle watch scheme
7.2	Reflections of traffic in shop windows
7.3	be ready to stop
7.4	gain speed on the hard shoulder before moving out onto the carriageway
7.5	High vehicles
7.6	stop and wait
7.7	Injury to another person
	Damage to someone's property
	Damage to other vehicles
7.8	The cyclist crossing the road
7.9	By changing to a lower gear
7.10	Edge of the carriageway
7.11	leave your sidelights on
7.12	Your first route may be blocked
7.13	Remove all valuables
7.14	between 11.30 pm and 7 am in a built-up area
7.15	With-flow pedal cycle lane
7.16	on your own
	on the motorway
7.17	Turn to the left
7.18	leave the motorway at the next exit
7.19	

7.20	Drive slowly past
	Give plenty of room
7.21	Crossroads
7.22	wait for them to cross
7.23	To get the best view of the road ahead
7.24	gently
7.25	In the vehicle handbook
7.26	wait in the box junction if your exit is clear
7.27	38 metres (125 feet)
7.28	Wait behind the long vehicle
7.29	To make them more visible in thick fog
7.30	be aware that the driver's reactions may not be as fast as yours
7.31	Be patient and wait
7.32	give way to the pedestrians who are already crossing
7.33	at any time
7.34	reassure them
	not leave them alone
7.35	No waiting zone ends